AND THE EARTH
TREMBLED

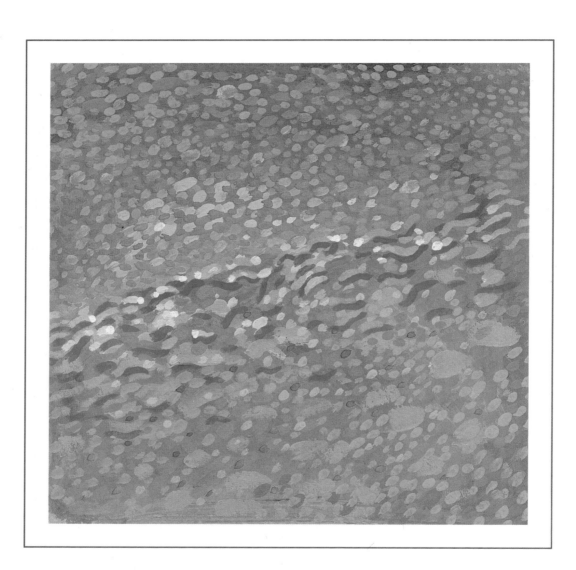

SHULAMITH LEVEY OPPENHEIM

AND THE EARTH
TREMBLED

The Creation of Adam and Eve

ILLUSTRATED BY

Neil Waldman

HARCOURT BRACE & COMPANY

San Diego   New York   London

For Ann, Patty, Jane, Barbara, Anna, Corinne.
—S. L. O.

For Jas, son of my palm.
—N. W.

Text copyright © 1996 by Shulamith Levey Oppenheim
Illustrations copyright © 1996 by Neil Waldman

Requests for permission to make copies of any part of the work should be mailed to:
Permissions Department, Harcourt Brace & Company, 6277 Sea Harbor Drive, Orlando, Florida 32887-6777.

Library of Congress Cataloging-in-Publication Data
Oppenheim, Shulamith Levey.
And the earth trembled: the creation of Adam and Eve/Shulamith Levey Oppenheim; illustrated by Neil Waldman.
p.   cm.
Summary: An Islamic version of the story of the creation of Adam and Eve.
ISBN 0-15-200025-9
1. Koran stories. [1. Koran stories. 2. Adam (Biblical figure) 3. Eve (Biblical figure)] I. Waldman, Neil, ill. II. Title.
BP130.58.O66   1996
297′.1—dc20   95-30829

The paintings in this book were done in acrylic paints on Arches cold-pressed watercolor paper.
The display type was set in Herculanum.
The text type was set in Weiss.
Printed and bound by Tien Wah Press, Singapore
This book was printed with soya-based inks on Leykam recycled paper, which contains
more than 20 percent postconsumer waste and has a total recycled content of at least 50 percent.
Production supervision by Warren Wallerstein and Pascha Gerlinger
Designed by Linda Lockowitz

First edition
A B C D E

Printed in Singapore

AUTHOR'S NOTE

AS WITH THE STORY of Adam and Eve and their banishment from Paradise, the best-known version of the creation of man and woman is in the Bible, in Genesis, the First Book of Moses. There, only a few short verses are devoted to this fateful act of God: "Then the Lord God formed man of the dust of the ground and breathed into his nostrils the breath of life . . . and the rib which the Lord God had taken from man, made he a woman and brought her unto man."

It is in the Book of Legends, the Haggadah in Hebrew, that we find an extended, embellished tale, containing a number of elements found also in this Islamic legend: the angels and the earth protesting mightily against the creation of man, fearing his destructive nature.

The Islamic version from which this story is retold can be found in the work of Abou-Djafar al Tabari, a famous Islamic scholar who was a religious authority and historian. Born about 839 A.D. in Amul, a city near the southern shore of the Caspian Sea, he traveled throughout the Islamic world and finally settled in Baghdad, in what is now Iraq. He acquired material for his history of the world from oral and literary sources, as well as from the Koran. The material for this particular version can be found in the Reverend S. Baring-Gould's wonderful book *Legends of the Patriarchs and Prophets* (New York, 1885).

OD PONDERED, "I have created the heavens and the earth and the oceans. I have fashioned angels and all manner of living creatures. But something is missing."

From dawn to dusk and from dusk to dawn, God pondered.

Then God realized what was wrong. Despite the angels, despite the heavens and the earth and the waters teeming with life, He was lonely.

"Therefore," He thought, "I shall create a being with a body made of flesh like the animals, but with intelligence, with a brain like the angels."

How delighted God was. His joy knew no bounds. Immediately He convened the angels and spelled out His purpose. But to His amazement, there was a great outcry, a vehement outcry among the multitude.

One angel took courage and came forward.

"Forgive us, for You are One and Most High and we are Your servants. But think what will come of this. We angels are transparent. Our every thought and feeling is revealed through our pure light. We have no choice but to reflect ourselves. Hence, we are honesty itself." Here the angel motioned for the others to come forward.

The angel continued, "If You embed a mind within a wall of flesh and bone, it will be hidden. Hidden, it will be prey to ugly desires. These desires will enslave the flesh even more. Think, O God, an animal kills from need. This creature will kill from greed, mark us!"

"Greed breeds jealousy. Jealousy leads to hatred," the angels echoed one another.

"And hatred"—here all the angels fell on their knees and covered their faces before God—"hatred ends in the red flames of war."

"And"—the first angel spoke again in hushed tones—"the beauty which we see around us, everywhere we look, that You have created, will be destroyed, without trace."

There followed a long silence.

Then God spoke.

"I thank you all for speaking up. I admit to much wisdom in your words. But I say Man must be created and you must worship him."

Now, the angels knew their Creator. With folded wings they withdrew.

Then God ordered His four archangels—Jibril, Mikail, Azrail, and Israil—to bring Him lumps of clay from the four quarters of Earth.

Together they descended to carry out God's command.

But to their amazement, Earth trembled at their appearance and demanded, "What are you about?"

To which they answered, "We are following God's command to fetch clay and dust that He may create Man."

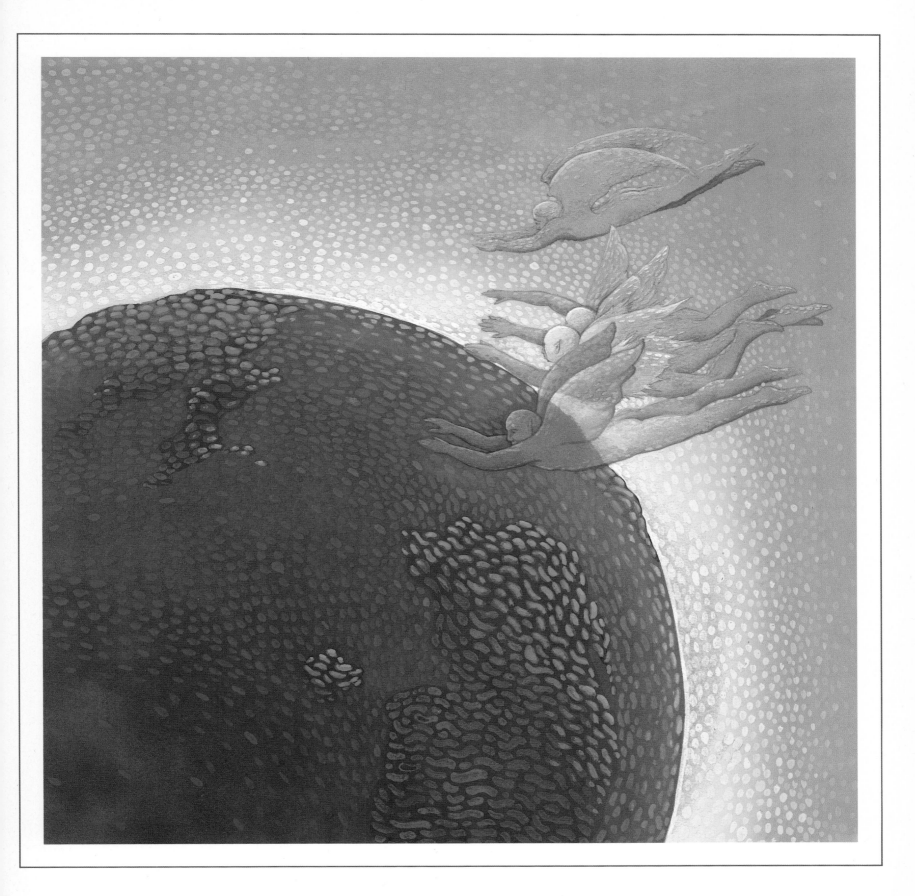

At these words there was a quaking from deep within the very heart of Earth, and Earth swore an oath by God.

"*Never* shall you take from me! What if such a creature turns on me and sheds innocent blood?"

Jibril and Mikail and Israil, seeing Earth's terror and respecting an oath sworn to God, returned empty-handed to God. But Azrail, the angel of death, stood firm and stooped to gather lumps of clay from the four quarters of Earth.

"Stop!" And this time Earth's cry was laced with pain. "Did I not tell you I cannot be party to the birth of evil?"

But the angel of death was deaf to Earth's pleas and tore clay from the body of Earth, saying, "It is God's wish, nay, even more, God's command—He who created you and created me. And there is nothing stronger than God's command."

Straight to heaven went Azrail with his prize. Seeing the clay, God praised him.

"You, Azrail, shall be My servant on earth. You, the angel of death, shall take the soul from Man, by force if necessary, when Man's time approaches. For this man whom I shall create will have many descendants."

So it was on Friday that God fashioned what He believed to be His masterpiece.

"From the clay of Mecca and Medina I shall form the head and the breast. For in Mecca, in a later age, shall be erected the Great Mosque, to contain the Black Stone that will be given by Jibril to Abraham. And in Medina shall be laid to rest in his tomb Muhammud, my messenger on earth. And from the rest of the clay and dust I shall form the body and the limbs."

In silence, clustered about the gates of Paradise, the angels observed how Man was fashioned, and they gazed in hushed reverence at the beauty of this yet lifeless being. Only Iblis, sensing the power and love God was bestowing on this particular creation, consumed with envy, scoffed and spat out for all to hear, "Fools, all of you! How can you admire a creation made of dirt?" This he repeated, louder and louder, but no one heeded his words.

For one moment it seemed as if God turned toward Iblis, but that moment passed, and long did the inhabitants of Paradise gaze in awe. Then with one voice they burst out in praise of their Creator.

Clearly, God was delighted, but He silenced them.

"Well and good that you see the wonder of this man, whom I shall call Adam. But note, he is not yet imbued with a living soul, the soul which I created ages before and which has been steeped in My light. SOUL!" God commanded, "Soul, enter into Adam's body!"

But to His astonishment, Soul held back.

"My Lord"—Soul's voice was like music—"I am loathe to exchange the boundless universe for a narrow home. This form frightens and repels me. It is dark and it is hollow."

Now God's fury knew no bounds. First the angels had balked at the idea of Man. Then Earth protested and wanted no part of Man's creation. And here was Soul, voicing a distinct disinclination to do His bidding.

Raging, God exclaimed, "Enter you must! But this shall be your fate. As you enter against your will, so shall you one day leave Man's body against your will."

And with violence God blew Soul through Adam's nostrils and into his head. And from his head Soul flew to Adam's tongue. Whereupon Adam read the inscription which was upon God's throne: "There is no god but God, and Muhammud is His messenger."

Now God's joy was boundless!

"Know, Adam, that for just such a purpose have I created you. You and your descendants shall worship Me."

Turning to the angels, God continued, and His voice thundered throughout the seven heavens, "I am a hidden treasure, and through your praise shall I be revealed on earth and in the sky and in the depths of the oceans. And it shall be from My hand that you come to know mercy and loving-kindness."

Then Soul journeyed to Adam's limbs, and he stood upright, his head reaching into the seventh heaven. There, the light emanating from God's throne was of such brightness that he shut his eyes.

"What light is this, O Eternal One?"

God answered, softly now, "It is the light of a prophet who shall spring from you in later times. And hear me, Adam, for I swear by My own honor"—and the angels and even Iblis, congregated nearby, trembled at God's own oath—"I swear that for him alone, for Muhammud, have I created the universe. In heaven he is called Ahmed, the much-praised one, but on earth he shall be called Muhammud. Only through belief in him as My messenger and the repository of My words shall men be led from falsehood to truth."

Now, God spoke these words because He was all-knowing. Just as He was quite aware that jealousy was eating away at the heart of Iblis, so He foresaw a time when, as the angels feared, greed and violence would overpower men, a time when His messenger, Muhammud, would appear to lead all men from error and darkness into virtue and light.

God then caused all living creatures to make obeisance before Adam.

"Over all living things do I give you dominion."

"And now"—God's voice was tired—"now come, My angels, come and bow down before Adam."

Israil was the first to obey. God rewarded him, placing in his charge the Book of Fate, in which men's deeds and their souls' destinies are recorded.

Only Iblis stood aside, bellowing out to God, "Why should I, O Greatest One, I, made of fire, bow down to one made of dust?"

This was, to God, the final defiance. In a burst of lightning, He cast Iblis out of the choir of angels and forbade him entrance into Paradise.

Then God turned to Adam and His voice was no more than a whisper. "Speak, My Adam, speak to the angels."

With surpassing wisdom, Adam spoke, ending, to God's delight, with eloquent words extolling the power and the majesty and the goodness of his Creator.

When Adam was finished, God bade the archangel Jibril to present Adam with a bunch of grapes from the vineyard in Paradise. Adam ate of the grapes and fell into a deep sleep.

While Adam slept and dreamed of another such as himself but different in the ways of male and female, God drew out Eve from Adam's left side. Eve, God named her, or Hava, for, as God explained, "Have I not extracted her from one who lives, from Hai, or 'Life'?"

And as He formed her, God instructed Himself, "And her eyes shall hold tenderness and her voice shall be all sweetness as the turtledove."

Then God laid Eve beside Adam and looked on her with pride and satisfaction.

"Is she not beautiful?" God was content with Himself.

And beautiful she was, resembling Adam as a twin resembles its other, except that her features were delicate. Her hair was long and it was divided into seven hundred locks. In form, God had taken care to fashion Eve more slender, smaller.

Then God touched Adam on his shoulder and Adam awoke.

Finding Eve at his side, Adam could only shake his head.

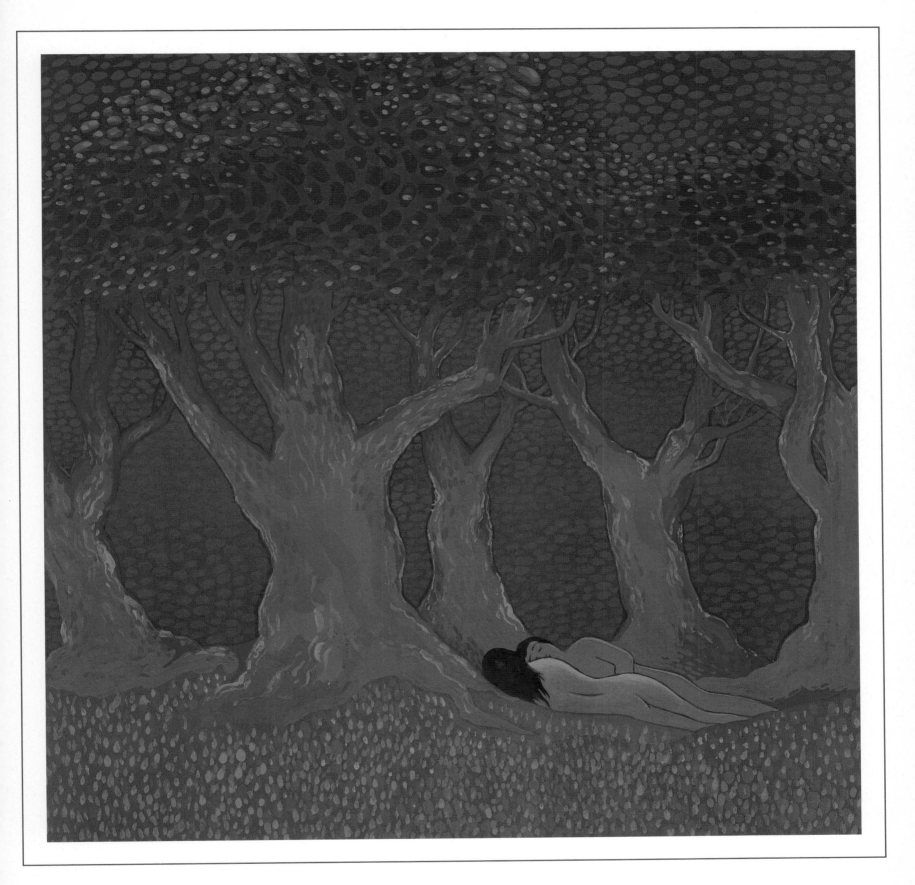

"Why am I amazed and yet not amazed?"

God smiled down on His two creations.

"Because you have been dreaming, have you not, of one such as she?"

Adam reached out to take Eve's hand.

Eve rose to her knees. Her face was radiant, but her voice was troubled.

"My love for you already is greater than yours for me. So have I been created. This I feel. I have been created to be your wife, yet it is God who is my master, and I cannot embrace you, nor let you embrace me, nor lay my head on your breast without His permission. Moreover"—and Eve blushed the first blush on earth—"should you not have a gift to present to your beloved?"

In an instant Adam rose to his feet and summoned Jibril to him.

"Go to your Maker. Ask Him if I may take Eve to wife. Beg of Him a gift that I may present to her as a bind for marriage."

In an eye's blink, Jibril was gone and returned.

"God rejoices that you, Adam, find His creation, Eve, agreeable. He exhorts you never to forget that she is your helpmate and you, hers. And you, Adam"—here Jibril raised his arms toward the seventh heaven—"you must both treat each other with kindness and respect and love. Above all, pray for Muhammud and the prophets to be born from your union with Eve."

When Jibril had finished, the angel Ridhwan, keeper of the gates of Paradise, appeared, leading the winged horse, Meimun, God's gift to Adam. And for Eve, the light-footed she-camel.

Jibril, Adam, and Eve thanked Ridhwan and bade him convey their obeisance to God. Then Jibril helped Adam and Eve to mount their steeds, and he himself led them into Paradise, where they were greeted by the angels and all Earth's living creatures and those of sky and sea, saying, "All hail to the mother and father of Muhammud."

It was Friday when Adam and Eve entered Paradise.

There in the midst of the garden was a green silk tent supported by golden pillars. Eve clapped her hands for the sheer joy of it all. She opened the folds of the tent, with Adam close behind her, and they beheld two golden thrones on a floral dais.

"First"—Jibril stopped them—"you must bathe in one of the rivers of Eden, and then you must come before God."

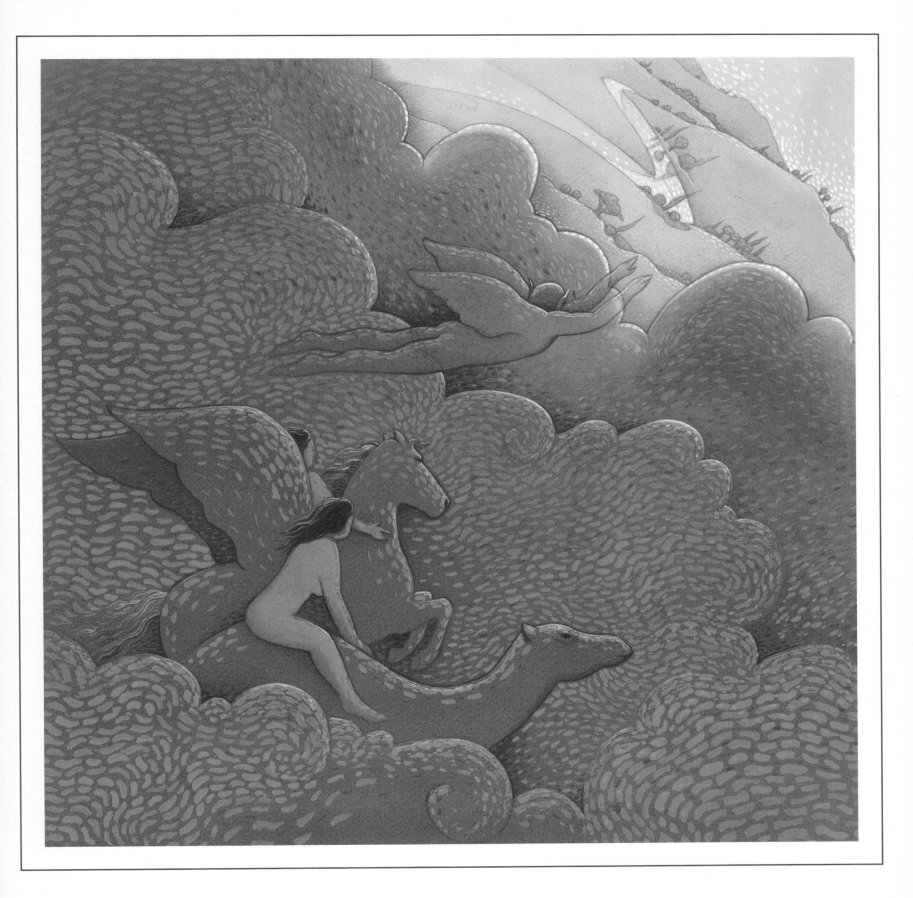

This was done. And when Adam and Eve stood before God, how filled with joy was His substance. And He said to them, "This garden will be your home. I Myself have prepared it. Here you are protected from all extremes, from heat and cold, from hunger and thirst, from all such excesses. Enjoy whatever meets your eye and pleases you, and truly there are wonders without number here. Only I implore you, nay, I command you, taste of all fruits except that of the wheat tree which centers the garden."

Adam and Eve bowed their heads.

But God was not through.

"This I shall share with you, for you are dearest to Me on earth. Iblis envies you. Jealousy eats away at his innards. He spends his waking hours seeking to destroy you by whatever means, subtle or otherwise. Be ever on your guard. Do not succumb to flattery. Believe only My word. Never forget this, as Iblis never forgets that it was because of you, Adam and Eve, that I cast him, Iblis, out of Paradise."

And Adam and Eve remained five hundred years in Paradise, living among all its inhabitants in peace and joy.